Dan's Plan

BOB BOOKS

Rhyming Words

Dan's Plan

by Lynn Maslen Kertell
pictures by Dana Sullivan

Scholastic Inc.

ISBN 978-0-545-51490-3

12 11   18 19 20/0
Printed in China   68

First printing, July 2013

Dan ran and ran.

Dan was hot.

Dan got a cap.

Dan was hot.

Dan had a plan.

Dan got a fan.

Dan got a tub and a can.

Not hot now, Dan!

The End

Word Family: AN

can
Dan
fan
plan
ran

Other words in this story:

a	hot
and	not
cap	now
got	tub
had	was

The Complete Bob Books® Series

READING READINESS

MY FIRST BOB BOOKS® ALPHABET

MY FIRST BOB BOOKS® PRE-READING SKILLS

STAGE 1: STARTING TO READ

SET 1 BEGINNING READERS

FIRST STORIES

SIGHT WORDS KINDERGARTEN

STAGE 2: EMERGING READER

SET 2 ADVANCING BEGINNERS

RHYMING WORDS

SIGHT WORDS FIRST GRADE

STAGE 3: DEVELOPING READER

SET 3 WORD FAMILIES

SET 4 COMPLEX WORDS

SET 5 LONG VOWELS

Lexile® Measure: AD30L
Guided Reading Level: C
Scholastic Reading Level: Grade 1
Word Count: 33

 Bob Books Apps are available for phones & tablets

www.BobBooks.com

Scholastic Inc.
978-0-545-51490-3

Cam's Snack

BOB BOOKS
Rhyming Words

Cam's Snack

by Lynn Maslen Kertell
pictures by Dana Sullivan

ISBN 978-0-545-51491-0

12 11   18 19 20/0
Printed in China   68

First printing, July 2013

Cam wants a snack.

Can Cam get jam?

Pam has jam.

Can Cam get a yam?

Gram has a yam.

Can Cam get a clam?

Pam has a clam.

A snack for Cam is eggs and ham.

The End

Word Family: AM

Cam
clam
Gram
ham
jam
Pam
yam

Other words in this story:

a	get
and	has
can	is
eggs	snack
for	wants

The Complete Bob Books® Series

READING READINESS

MY FIRST
BOB BOOKS®
ALPHABET

MY FIRST
BOB BOOKS®
PRE-READING
SKILLS

STAGE 1: STARTING TO READ

SET 1
BEGINNING
READERS

FIRST
STORIES

SIGHT WORDS
KINDERGARTEN

STAGE 2: EMERGING READER

SET 2
ADVANCING
BEGINNERS

RHYMING
WORDS

SIGHT WORDS
FIRST GRADE

STAGE 3: DEVELOPING READER

SET 3
WORD
FAMILIES

SET 4
COMPLEX
WORDS

SET 5
LONG
VOWELS

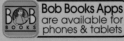
Bob Books Apps
are available for
phones & tablets

www.BobBooks.com

Lexile® Measure: AD280L
Guided Reading Level: D
Scholastic Reading Level: Grade 1
Word Count: 37

Scholastic Inc.
978-0-545-51491-0

The Hen in the Den

SCHOLASTIC

The Hen in the Den

by Lynn Maslen Kertell
pictures by Dana Sullivan

Scholastic Inc.

ISBN 978-0-545-51493-4

Copyright © 2013 by Lynn Maslen Kertell. All rights reserved. Published by Scholastic Inc. by arrangement with Bob Books® New Initiatives LLC. SCHOLASTIC and associated logos are trademarks and/or registered trademarks of Scholastic Inc. BOB BOOKS are trademarks and/or registered trademarks of Bob Books Publications LLC.

Lexile® is a registered trademark of MetaMetrics, Inc.

12 11   18 19 20/0
Printed in China   68

First printing, July 2013

The hen was in the den.

Ken was in the den.

"Go in the pen, hen."

5

The hen did not go in the pen.

6

Ten men went to the hen.

The hen went in the pen.

The hen sat on a nest.

The hen had eggs.

The End

Word Family: EN

den
hen
Ken
men
pen
ten

Other words in this story:

a	in	the
did	nest	to
eggs	not	was
go	on	went
had	sat	

The Complete Bob Books® Series

READING READINESS

MY FIRST
BOB BOOKS®
ALPHABET

MY FIRST
BOB BOOKS®
PRE-READING
SKILLS

STAGE 1: STARTING TO READ

SET 1
BEGINNING
READERS

FIRST
STORIES

SIGHT WORDS
KINDERGARTEN

STAGE 2: EMERGING READER

SET 2
ADVANCING
BEGINNERS

RHYMING
WORDS

SIGHT WORDS
FIRST GRADE

STAGE 3: DEVELOPING READER

SET 3
WORD
FAMILIES

SET 4
COMPLEX
WORDS

SET 5
LONG
VOWELS

Bob Books Apps
are available for
phones & tablets

www.BobBooks.com

Lexile® Measure: AD140L
Guided Reading Level: E
Scholastic Reading Level: Grade 1
Word Count: 46

Scholastic Inc.
978-0-545-51490-3

The Red Sled

Rhyming
Words
Book 4

BOB
BOOKS
Rhyming Words

SCHOLASTIC

The Red Sled

by Lynn Maslen Kertell
pictures by Dana Sullivan

Scholastic Inc.

ISBN 978-0-545-51492-7

Copyright © 2013 by Lynn Maslen Kertell. All rights reserved. Published by Scholastic Inc. by arrangement with Bob Books® Publications, LLC. SCHOLASTIC and associated logos are trademarks and/or registered trademarks of Scholastic Inc. BOB BOOKS are trademarks and/or registered trademarks of Bob Books® Publications, LLC.

12 11   18 19 20/0
Printed in China   68
First printing, July 2013

The red sled sped.

It sped on a hill.

It hit a shed!

5

Get up, Ted.

6

Get up, Fred.

Go to bed, Fred and Ted.

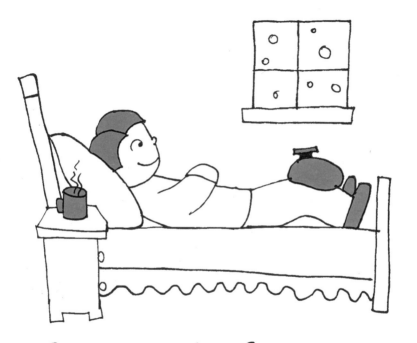

Put up your leg. Get a rest.

9

Fred and Ted get back on the sled.

The End

Word Family: ED

bed
Fred
red
shed
sled
sped
Ted

Other words in this story:

a	hit	the
and	it	to
back	leg	up
get	on	your
go	put	
hill	rest	

12

The Complete Bob Books® Series

READING READINESS

MY FIRST
BOB BOOKS®
ALPHABET

MY FIRST
BOB BOOKS®
PRE-READING
SKILLS

STAGE 1: STARTING TO READ

SET 1
BEGINNING
READERS

FIRST
STORIES

SIGHT WORDS
KINDERGARTEN

STAGE 2: EMERGING READER

SET 2
ADVANCING
BEGINNERS

RHYMING
WORDS

SIGHT WORDS
FIRST GRADE

STAGE 3: DEVELOPING READER

SET 3
WORD
FAMILIES

SET 4
COMPLEX
WORDS

SET 5
LONG
VOWELS

Lexile® Measure: AD30L
Guided Reading Level: D
Scholastic Reading Level: Grade 1
Word Count: 40

 Bob Books Apps
are available for
phones & tablets

www.BobBooks.com

Drip, Drip, Drip

BOB BOOKS

Rhyming Words

Drip, Drip, Drip

by Lynn Maslen Kertell
pictures by Dana Sullivan

Scholastic Inc.

ISBN 978-0-545-51494-1

12 11
Printed in China
First printing, July 2013

18 19 20/0
68

The sun is hot.

Kip and Jip run and skip.

Kip and Jip want a drink.

"Drip, drip, drip."

"Yip, yip, yip!"

Kip licks his lips.

Jip grins. Jip drags a pan.

Kip and Jip get a sip.

The End

Word Family: IP

drip	sip
Jip	skip
Kip	yip
lip	

Other words in this story:

a	licks
and	pan
drag	run
drink	sun
get	the
grin	want
his	was
hot	

The Complete Bob Books® Series

READING READINESS

MY FIRST
BOB BOOKS®
ALPHABET

MY FIRST
BOB BOOKS®
PRE-READING
SKILLS

STAGE 1: STARTING TO READ

SET 1
BEGINNING
READERS

FIRST
STORIES

SIGHT WORDS
KINDERGARTEN

STAGE 2: EMERGING READER

SET 2
ADVANCING
BEGINNERS

RHYMING
WORDS

SIGHT WORDS
FIRST GRADE

STAGE 3: DEVELOPING READER

SET 3
WORD
FAMILIES

SET 4
COMPLEX
WO

Bob Books a
are availa
phones &

www.BobBoo

Lexile® Measure: AD290L
Guided Reading Level: D
Scholastic Reading Level: Grade 1
Word Count: 38

Lin in the Bin

SCHOLASTIC

BOB BOOKS

Rhyming Words

Lin in the Bin

by Lynn Maslen Kertell
pictures by Dana Sullivan

Scholastic Inc.

ISBN 978-0-545-51495-8

12 11   18 19 20/0
Printed in China   68

First printing, July 2013

Lin is in the bin.

Lin has a pin.

4

Lin can spin and spin.

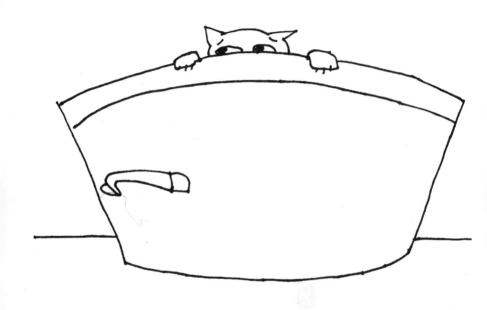

The bin is tin.

Lin is in a fix.

Lin did a flip and a skip.

The bin did tip.

Lin did grin.

The End

Word Family: IN

bin
grin
Lin
pin
spin
tin

Other words in this story:

a	fix	is
and	flip	skip
can	has	the
did	in	tip

The Complete Bob Books® Series

READING READINESS

MY FIRST
BOB BOOKS®
ALPHABET

MY FIRST
BOB BOOKS®
PRE-READING
SKILLS

STAGE 1: STARTING TO READ

SET 1
BEGINNING
READERS

FIRST
STORIES

SIGHT WORDS
KINDERGARTEN

STAGE 2: EMERGING READER

SET 2
ADVANCING
BEGINNERS

RHYMING
WORDS

SIGHT WORDS
FIRST GRADE

STAGE 3: DEVELOPING READER

SET 3
WORD
FAMILIES

Bob Books
are availa
phone

www.BobB

Lexile® Measure: AD120L
Guided Reading Level: E
Scholastic Reading Level: Grade 1
Word Count: 37

The Dog in the Fog

BOB BOOKS

Rhyming Words

The Dog in the Fog

by Lynn Maslen Kertell
pictures by Dana Sullivan

Scholastic Inc.

ISBN 978-0-545-51496-5

12 11   18 19 20/0
Printed in China   68

First printing, July 2013

A dog jogs to a bog.

The bog is full of fog.

The dog finds a frog.

The frog is in the fog.

6

The dog finds a hog.

A log is in the fog.

The dog gets on the log.

The dog, frog, and hog jog on the log.

The End

Word Family: OG

bog
dog
fog
frog
hog
jogs

Other words in this story:

a
finds
full
is
of
on
the
to

The Complete Bob Books® Series

READING READINESS

MY FIRST
BOB BOOKS®
ALPHABET

MY FIRST
BOB BOOKS®
PRE-READING
SKILLS

STAGE 1: STARTING TO READ

SET 1
BEGINNING
READERS

FIRST
STORIES

SIGHT WORDS
KINDERGARTEN

STAGE 2: EMERGING READER

SET 2
ADVANCING
BEGINNERS

RHYMING
WORDS

SIGHT WORDS
FIRST GRADE

STAGE 3

Lexile® Measure: AD270L
Guided Reading Level: E
Scholastic Reading Level: Grade 1
Word Count: 49

The Spot

BOB BOOKS

Rhyming Words

The Spot

by Lynn Maslen Kertell
pictures by Dana Sullivan

Scholastic Inc.

ISBN 978-0-545-51497-2

12 11   18 19 20/0
Printed in China   68

First printing, July 2013

Dot has a doll.

The doll is on the cot.

The doll is in the pot.

The doll got a spot.

No, no, not a spot!

7

Dot rubs the spot.

Dot rubs the spot a lot.

9

No spot on the doll, Dot!

10

The End

Word Family: OT

cot
Dot
got
lot
not
pot
spot

Other words in this story:

a	no
doll	on
has	rubs
in	the
is	

In a Huff

by Lynn Maslen Kertell
pictures by Dana Sullivan

Scholastic Inc.

ISBN 978-0-545-51498-9

12 11   18 19 20/0
Printed in China   68

First printing, July 2013

Muff is a cat.

Muff is in a huff.

4

Ruff runs. Ruff tags.

5

Ruff is too gruff.

Muff is stuck.

Muff has a plan!

Fluff! Puff!

9

Muff purrs.

The End

Word Family: UFF

fluff
gruff
huff
Muff
puff
Ruff

Other words in this story:

a	is	tags
cat	plan	too
has	purrs	stuck
in	runs	

Bug and Pug

by Lynn Maslen Kertell
pictures by Dana Sullivan

Scholastic Inc.

ISBN 978-0-545-51499-6

12 11   18 19 20/0
Printed in China   68
First printing, July 2013

Bug has a jug.

Bug tugs on the jug.

Pug has a rug.

Pug rolls on the rug.

Pug has a mug.

Pug tugs on the jug.

Pug has the mug and the jug.

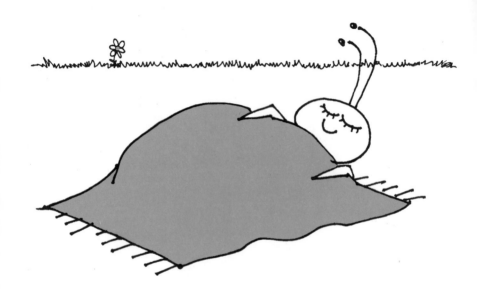

Bug is as snug as a bug in a rug.

The End

Word Family: UG

Bug
jug
mug
Pug
rug
snug
tugs

Other words in this story:

a	is
and	on
as	rolls
has	the

The Complete Bob Books® Series

READING READINESS

MY FIRST BOB BOOKS® ALPHABET

MY FIRST BOB BOOKS® PRE-READING SKILLS

STAGE 1: STARTING TO READ

SET 1 BEGINNING READERS

FIRST STORIES

SIGHT WORDS KINDERGARTEN

STAGE 2: EMERGING READER

SET 2 ADVANCING BEGINNERS

RHYMING WORDS

SIGHT WORDS FIRST GRADE

STAGE 3: DEVELOPING READER

SET 3 WORD FAMILIES

SET 4 COMPLEX WORDS

SET 5 LONG VOWELS

Lexile® Measure: AD360L
Guided Reading Level: E
Scholastic Reading Level: Grade 1
Word Count: 44

Bob Books Apps are available for phones & tablets

www.BobBooks.com

Scholastic Inc.
978-0-545-51499-6